Dedicated to the men and women who patrol our nation's prisons, jails and juvenile detention facilities.

Brian Dawe
American Correctional
Officer Intelligence Network

www.COIntel.net ACOIN1@aol.com 307-880-9000

MY DAD'S A HERO...

MY DAD'S A

CORRECTIONAL OFFICER

Published by Probity Press ISBN 978-0-9851985-3-4 First Edition 2014
1. Children. 2. Corrections. 3. Correctional Officers — Title 2014

This book is available at quantity discounts for bulk purchases.
For information call 631-858-1600

PROBITY PRESS
New York

Our Dad is different.
He knows a lot of criminals.
Dad is in charge of a lot of people.
Mommy says daddy is sometimes
in danger.

Dad wears a uniform, has a badge and got special training in a school called an academy.

Dad is part of the law that includes police officers and judges.

When someone does something bad, they have to live in a place away from everyone else. The place is called a prison and the people who have to live there are called prisoners.

Prisoners can be men or they can be women.
They can be very mean
and do not always follow rules.

Dad helps criminals learn that it is good to follow the rules and not hurt anyone.

Dad makes sure they are nice to each other and have respect for the law.

Dad sometimes works long hours.

He often misses holidays and family time.
Mom helps us understand when we
are feeling sad and miss daddy.

But my Dad protects the world by keeping criminals in prison. Dad has a very important job.

Some prisoners want to change, and my Dad helps them learn how to make their life better.

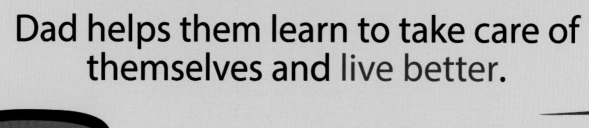

Dad helps them learn to take care of themselves and live better.

Dad helps them go to school.

He helps them learn how to do different jobs so they can work when they leave prison.

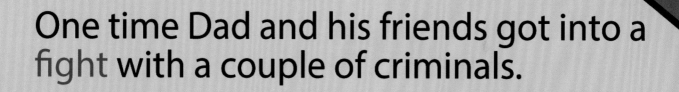

One time Dad and his friends got into a fight with a couple of criminals.

They won the fight, but Dad and his friend had to stay in the hospital for a couple of nights.

He had some broken bones and we would catch him staring a lot.

But he got better and was
our same old Dad again.

My Dad's a Hero...

My Dad's a Correctional Officer!

My Dad's a Hero…My Dad's a Correctional Officer
A Parent's Guide to Teaching From This Book

Your child will be excited about a book devoted to his or her parent's job. We suggest you start by sitting down and reading the book to your child as you would any children's book. Each page can be a starting point for discussion about your job, or elicit questions from your child about what you do. Your son or daughter may ask you outright, "Do you do that?" Take your time and answer your child's questions honestly. It is also possible that your son or daughter may simply sit quietly, enjoying the story, the illustrations, and the time they're spending with you. Bring the book out often to read again. This is a book that celebrates the marvelous work you do. Have fun with it.

Your job is a different one and here we introduce that concept to children. Introduce the idea of controlling others and how that is not a bad thing. Also, remember your children may not understand things like "danger" so tread lightly but make sure they understand. It may be important for your child to understand there is some danger in your job in case you ever get injured.

- How is being a correctional officer different from other jobs?
    - o Does everyone wear a uniform, badge and carry a gun?
    - o Is there a structure with different ranks like in the Army?"
    - o Do we have to work when a lot of other fathers are home, like weekends and holidays?
- What does it mean to control other people?
    - o Is it always bad to have someone control parts of your life? When is it good?
    - o Who controls you? Or Mommy? Or Daddy?
- What does it mean to be in "danger?"
    - o Why does Mommy worry about Daddy?
    - o Have you ever been in danger?
    - o Does being in danger mean you have to be extra careful?

Correctionl work is the part of the justice system. In a system, everyone has a role. You are specially trained to do your job. Try to make the child understand the role of the correctional officer. You walk the toughest "beat" in law enforcement and don't be afraid to let people, particularly your child, know this about you.

- What kind of special training do you think Daddy got to be a correctional officer?
    - o Do you think they taught Daddy how to protect himself?
    - o Do you think they taught Daddy how to think better?
    - o Do you think they taught Daddy how to use weapons?
- What do we mean by the justice system?
    - o Why do we have a justice system?
    - o What are the jobs of people in the justice system?
    - o Where does Daddy's job fit in the justice system?

It is time to introduce the idea of "who" goes to jail and "why." Be careful not to scare your child, but let them know that the people in jail are not always the nicest people in society and need to be controlled. Let your child know there is teamwork to control the prisoners if needed.

- What kinds of things do people do that put them in prison?
    - Is it nice to hurt other people?
    - Is it nice to steal from other people?
    - What happens when someone hurts you or steals from you?
- Why is Dad left alone with the prisoners?
    - What does it mean to be part of a team?
    - Do you feel safer when you are with a team of people against one person?

Working in correctional jobs requires a demand on the family that includes long hours and missing family activities. A spouse of a correctional officer has to be very patient and remind their children that the correctional job is important to the world. Making the prison popuation become able to function in society takes a lot of dedication and constant reminders to prisoners to act in a civil manner. This is the job of the correctional officer.

- How does Daddy make prisoners act nicer to each other?
    - Do you think telling them just one time is enough for prisoners to change?
    - Do you think the way Daddy acts has an effect on the prisoners' behavior?
    - Have you ever had to be told more than once how to act before you started to act right?
- Can you think of one time Daddy has missed something fun or important to you?
    - What do you think he did that day?
    - Do you think Daddy would have rather been with you?

Correctional officers don't just babysit criminals, but teach them how to live on the outside when they are released. Introduce the concept of rehabilitating criminals and making criminals into useful citizens who do not commit crimes against others.

- How does helping prisoners learn to clean up help them when they get out of prison?
    - Do people want to hire employees who are dirty?
    - What kind of job can a prisoner get when he gets out of jail?
- Why would prisoners go to school in jail?
    - Does a good education help you get a good job?
    - Are prisoners happy to be in school?
- What kind of jobs can prisoners have in jail?
    - Are there jobs to make and serve food?
    - Are there jobs to clean around the jail?
    - Are there jobs to learn how to build things?
    - What other jobs can you think of?

At some point while working in the prison system, the correetional officer will come across a fight and may have to defned themslves. During these times, life can be very scary for a child if the child is not prepared in advance. Let the child know that you have a team of men and women and that you have gear to protect you. Let them know you can see a doctor if you get injured. But mostly, let them know you will be alright in the end. This next slide might bring out the following questions:

- Sometimes there are fights in prisons. What does Daddy do to help himself in a fight?
    - What does Daddy wear? Or carry?
    - Do you think the other officers Daddy works with stand by and watch when there is a fight or do they help out?
- Why is fighting sometimes part of Daddy's job?
    - Do you think he learned about fighting in the academy?
    - What many things does Daddy do to avoid a fight in prison?

When a fight takes place, there is sometimes a serious injury. This part of the book is addressing an injury and some of the psychological effects that might occur. Dad is in the hospital with what appears to be a broken leg and has a little post-traumatic stress disorder which is very common among correctional officers. We want your child to be aware of this possibility, but also to know that Dad will get better with the love of his family and good medical care. Embrace the concern from these pages, but let your child know you will be better in the end.

- What do you think that happened to the correctional officer in the story?
    - How is he feeling?
    - What is he thinking?
- What do you think made him better in the story?
    - Did his doctors help?
    - Did his family help?
    - Do you remember a time when you were injured and got better?

Without correctional officers, we would be forced to put criminals back on the streets. This points to how important your job really is for everyone. Let your child look closely at this page and help them realize that the work you do is essential for society to function the way it does.

- Can you find the various crimes being committed in this picture?
    - What is the man with the gun trying to do?
    - What is the guy by the car doing?
    - Why is that guy carrying a TV set?
    - If we didn't have prisons and correctional officers, would all these people be in the neighborhood?
    - Is that a good thing?

Then come to the conclusion: